Financial Success Workbook

A Scriptural Program For Managing Your Resources

By Dr. Kurt Grosser

Abundant Freedom Press
Aurora, Colorado

Cover design by Archer Ellison, Inc.

Interior design and editing by Cynthia Arbuckle

Scripture referenced NASB are taken from the New American Standard Bible®. Copyright © The Lockman Foundation 1960,1962,1963,1968,1971,1972,1973,1975, 1977. Used by permission.

Scripture referenced NKJV are taken from the New King James Version®. Copyright © 1982 by Thomas Nelson, Inc. Used by permission. All rights reserved.

Scripture referenced NLT are taken from the Holly Bible, New Living Translation®, Copyright © 1996.Used by permission of Tyndale House Publishers, Inc. Wheaton, Illinois 60189. All rights reserved.

Scripture referenced NIV are taken from the Holy Bible, New International Version, Copyright © 1973,1978,1984. Used by permission of Zondervan Publishing House. All rights reserved.

Printed in the United States of America

Please visit our website for other titles and contact information:
www.AbundantFreedomMinistries.com

Abundant Freedom Press
P.O. Box 461316
Aurora, CO 80046

Dedication

This book is dedicated to all who are striving to live in financial freedom. Freedom from the bondage of the financial limitations imposed by our economic system. Freedom to live the abundant life and in the prosperity promised in the Word of God.

2 Corinthians 3:17 (NASB)
Now the Lord is the Spirit; and where the Spirit of the Lord is, there is liberty.

Acknowledgements

Special thanks to Kathy, my wife, and our children for their patience, understanding and endless encouragement.

Contents

Introduction to Designing your Spending Plan

In This Book

* Determining where you are

* Determine your assets

* Determine your liabilities

* Determine your net worth

* Determine your income

* Determine your expenditures

Determining where you are

In this book we will take a look at the mechanics of designing schedules and clerical methods of completing a spending plan. The techniques and approaches discussed are adaptable to any enterprise, whether a household, business, or other organization. The actual examples are representative of a household budget or spending plan.

Before designing a spending plan, we need to review some fundamentals concerned directly with the effectiveness of this process.

Family involvement entails cooperation, support, confidence, participation, and a common desire to achieve control over our finances. All family members, but principally the parents, with the exception of small children, must understand the broad objectives of the family plan; be convinced that their particular approach to managing the budget is preferable for their situation; be willing to devote the effort required to make it work and to support the program in all respects. The family must be willing to adapt to clear-cut lines of authority and responsibility. For example, God tells us that next to Jesus, the man is head of the household. With that position of authority comes responsibility to work as the primary provider. The wife has authority and certain responsibility.

Since budgeting in many respects includes controls and measurements of actual results against the planned objectives, we must be willing to responsibly account for what is taking place. Comparisons between a spending plan and actual results are meaningless unless the same expense classifications are used.

Our financial goals should be subjected to and in harmony with our long-range family plan. The spending plan should be realistic in expectations and flexible to unexpected changes. Effective planning and control of a budget requires that all family members have the same understanding of goals and responsibilities. Full and open communication is essential to sound family budget management. Only when we have a firm understanding of the fundamentals discussed here should we proceed with budget schedules.

God tells us that next to Jesus, the man is head of the household. With that position of authority comes responsibility to work as the primary provider.

To effectively determine where we are, we need to review the current monthly income and the expenditures of the past several months. To determine our present financial position or net worth, we have to account for our assets, which are things we possess, and our liabilities, which are debts we owe. The mathematical difference between our assets and our liabilities represents our net worth.

Some expenses, such as vacations and auto repairs, do not come due every month.
Estimate how much you spend for these on a yearly basis, divide that amount by twelve, and fill in the appropriate categories on the Expenditures Analysis Schedule.

Armed with this information you can calculate your present position and prepare an accurate spending plan of what you will be earning and spending. Do not be discouraged! Almost every spending plan is started with expenditures in excess of income.

We recommend that you take your check book(s), review each check and group them by expenditure category. This exercise will help you as a family to determine where you are. In the following chapters we will continue to work through the budgeting process.

Please pray that the Lord may give you guidance and wisdom, and especially patience as you work through these forms, and remember: from our past experience we have learned that in every case where families work together to fill in these schedules, they experienced fierce spiritual battles. Satan wants to keep us in financial bondage, whereas God wants us to be responsible stewards. We need to pray and keep looking to Him for help.

Evaluating your financial situation

When we begin to evaluate our *past* spending habit, every form of reasoning, defensiveness, and frustration will surface. When we examine our *present* financial position, depending on the result, we either feel defeated and discouraged, or proud and boastful of our accomplishments. God forgives us our past transgressions, and we cannot change anything in the past even if we want to. God's Word says that the old has gone and the new has come. That means that through Jesus Christ we have a new beginning.

We need God's guidance in evaluating our present financial situation. The Lord knows our hearts and motives and attitudes better than we do. It is for this reason that we must surrender ourselves to Him for guidance and direction.

We need to ask ourselves why we are willing to evaluate our financial situation. Is the reason to balance the numbers in our budget? Is the reason to solve a current financial crisis?

As an accountant, I know that *a budget is only as good as the preparer's willingness to follow it.* When we are sincere about wanting to change our old habits, and when we are willing to live within the limits and flexibilities of our means, only then should we proceed.

I have seen numerous examples where people said they wanted a budget to start living within their means. They wanted God's guidance and direction. The problem is that they never really let go and let God. Once their present crisis passed they continued in their former ways. In Romans it tells us that the Word is the power of God, and that revealed in it is His righteousness from faith to faith. That means that it takes faith or belief in the Word from one end to the other.

Are we ready to accept and believe what God's Word says about our finances?

Are we ready to act upon what the Word says?

Are we willing to stand firm and not subject ourselves to our old ways?

God knows our hearts and motives and attitudes better than we do. It is for this reason that we must surrender ourselves to Him for guidance and direction.

Let us search our hearts—The following scriptures will give us some statements of policy to follow for this:

When we begin to evaluate our past spending habits, every form of reasoning, defensiveness, and frustration will surface.

Remember, the Lord is our source—Jeremiah 17:5-10 states: "Thus says the Lord, cursed is the man who trusts in mankind and makes the flesh his strength, and whose heart turns away from the Lord. For he will be like a bush in the desert and will not see when prosperity comes, but will live in stony wastes in the wilderness, a land of salt without inhabitant. Blessed is the man who trusts in the Lord. For he will be like a tree planted by the water, that extends its roots by a stream and will not fear when the heat comes; but its leaves will be green, and it will not be anxious in a year of drought nor cease to yield fruit. The heart is more deceitful than all else and is desperately sick; who can understand it? I, the Lord, search the heart, I test the mind, even to give to each man according to his ways, according to the results of his deeds."

We need to build our patience and endurance—A spending plan is only as good as the preparer's willingness to follow it.

Setting your priorities

Before we begin to choose our financial priorities, we need to remind ourselves who we are in Christ and what that means. There are many scriptures that reveal that *God has a chosen plan (a path) for us.* Are we ready to accept and believe what God's Word says about our finances?

What choices do we have when we are setting our priorities? God has made all our important choices for us, as we see in the above scriptures. The only choice we have is to walk by our own free will in darkness and perish, or to choose His plan and path for us and succeed. When setting our priorities we must choose God first, and then walk by His Word and He will do the rest.

There are some things we have to do—such as living within the limits of our income. This can be done if we learn to rearrange our spending priorities.

It should also become a priority for us to get out of debt. We might review the list of things that we possess. We could sell those things we do not need and apply the proceeds toward the debt.

Implementing a spending plan

The budget, or spending plan, which we choose to implement for our family should be carefully structured within our income limitation. The expenditures budget that follows has four columns. Each line item should be discussed with family members, and upon mutual agreement, categorized as either of the following:

Need to have—are things that are absolutely essential.

Should have—are very necessary or important. However, they could be done without if it were absolutely necessary.

Would like to have—are necessary, but could be done without at the present time.

When the total expenditures exceed our income, we need to cut back first from the category of "Would like to have," until the objective within our means is accomplished.

Some expenses, such as vacations and auto repairs, do not come due every month. Estimate how much you spend for these on a yearly basis, divide that amount by twelve, and fill in the appropriate categories on the Expenditures Analysis Schedule.

Remember, we cannot spend more than what God has entrusted to us as His stewards. He knows every need and has promised to meet each one. In order to stay in financial freedom, it is important to develop and implement a spending plan. It is equally important to stick to it. We have to follow through and compare our actual income and expenditures to the budget to measure progress.

Persistence will bring success. A budget needs to be flexible and workable. When we evaluate our progress, we need to remember that we cannot change anything in the past; we can only change today and things in the future. *It takes an act of our will to accept freedom.* It also takes *an act of our will* to continue to stay in financial freedom.

Jesus has set us free. We are free indeed. Now that we accept that God's Word in us has made us free, we need to realize that the thief (Satan) comes and steals from us. Since we live in this world and are constantly subjected to the flesh, we need to stay in the Word of God and feed on it daily. As Jesus said, we need to deny our selfish nature and take up our cross (commitment)

daily. To walk in the freedom of the Word is now our way.

The Spending Plan

This workbook is a tool to help you establish spending priorities. It is a roadmap, a plan or guide to rebuild your life to achieve the financial freedom that was given to believers in Christ Jesus. A spending plan will help you establish boundaries and control your spending. It will help you plan where your money is going to go—instead of simply finding out where it went.

Often when faced with a financial crisis, we seek quick solutions. As soon as the crisis is over, we revert to our old habits until the next crisis comes. Does this sound familiar to you? It is our human nature to resist change and to put it off.

This workbook is designed to be used as a suggested step-by-step approach to make lasting changes in your life until the process is completed. To begin with, you need to review your spending history. Before you can determine your goals for financial freedom, you must understand where you are and how your existing financial system operates.

We believe that for each of us to reach financial freedom, we must examine our lives as individuals, how we relate to God as we function in our households, and in the work we do. Our finances are the fruit of our labor and the direct result of how we conduct our lives.

Scriptures tell us that we cannot serve God and mammon—meaning possessions or money. When we sort through our priorities and rearrange them according to scriptural principles, we will see the solutions as if someone (God) turned the lights on for us.

For a comprehensive study of scriptural principles for your finances, refer to our book, *Scriptural Principles for Financial Success*.

Change is a process

Developing successful financial control habits requires slow, steady progress toward specific goals that have a clear benefit for you. Setting a series of specific, achievable, short-term goals will help you make success a habit. After you have accomplished these goals and get used to the changes, add new goals to your list. By writing down specific goals, you will increase your chances of taking action. Consider possible rewards after certain goals are achieved. This gradual process will help you make the necessary lifestyle changes.

Small successes will add up to big rewards

Schedule regular rewards

Reinforce the behavior and attitude changes you make regarding your finances. Recognize the benefits of better saving and spending habits by adding rewards for accomplishing short-term goals.

Stay on track

Managing your income and expenditures isn't easy—and avoiding buying on credit is even more of an accomplishment!

Suggestions for making your financial habits and lifestyle changes into permanent habits include:

* Becoming successful
* Accepting God's blessings
* Maintaining motivation
* Getting support from others
* Managing stress
* Recovering from relapses
* Handling special occasions
* Staying on the right track

Becoming successful

Who is successful over the long-term in controlling their finances? If you know someone who is successful, find out what they do. Then do what they do.

Successful stewards:

* Set achievable goals
* Know that success is motivating and take time to plan for it
* Have a sense of accountability toward their spending and financial plan
* Make mistakes and learn from them
* Develop specific strategies to deal with individual problem areas

Accepting God's blessings

God wants to bless you. Blessed is he who trusts in the Lord. If you work on increasing your trust in Him, He will increase your blessings.

Maintain motivation

Budgets don't make a difference—people do. A positive approach doesn't just happen. Try a few of the following ideas to keep your motivation on track.

* Prayer—ask God to help you stay committed

* Fight spending fatigue

* It is easy to get into a rut—try new short-term goals

* Modify your plan periodically to keep it fresh

* Toss out what doesn't work—as you change, your goals and plans need to be updated too

* Take a break

* Your level of attention and commitment to change doesn't have to be constant. Alternating periods of intense effort, and a more relaxed approach can keep financial management from becoming another source of stress.

Getting support from others

Seek and identify sources of support and communicate your goals to them. Remember, it is easier to change things than people. Control what you can. Change your spending habits and lifestyle to fit your needs, not to conform to those of others. Recognize that some people in your life can be threatened by the changes you have made and are making. Avoid discussing your financial goals and spending plans with these people.

As a family, work together using the team approach. Remember, a house divided against itself will not stand, but a house united cannot fail.

Managing stress

Using money to feel better or to manage stress is a learned behavior and can be changed. Unfortunately, the pleasurable feelings we associate with buying something are usually short-lived and often followed by feelings of guilt.

If you have been using binge spending as a stress management tool, just abandoning it will leave a gap. You can fall back into your old habit quickly unless you replace it with a new approach to managing your feelings.

There are many kinds of destructive self talk that can keep your negative lifestyle cycles going. To make a change, you need to change your self talk.

For example:

Negative self talk	Positive self talk
I am too busy to change my lifestyle	I can make choices about how I want to live
I can't stop buying on credit	I can do all things through Christ who strengthens me
I am deprived—poor me	I can set realistic goals that lead to a better financial future

Recovering from relapses

The actual overspending binge isn't really the biggest problem; it is how you react to it that counts. Getting a bit off track can be frightening, but staying calm and learning from the situation is a valuable lesson. Quickly retracing your steps and getting back on track is very important. Wandering further down the wrong route will only make the path back harder to find.

Handling special occasions

Holidays and other special occasions can create complicated and stressful situations. Try spending limits or alternatives. It's what you do on a daily basis that really counts. Planning ahead and moderation are the keys to spending on holidays and special occasions.

Staying on the right track

A well planned budget and a confident approach will make managing your finances rewarding. A realistic budget, choices, and spending controls mixed with motivation, will guide you toward financial success.

As your path becomes clearer and you learn how to handle the bumps and curves ahead, even your most difficult situations will become surmountable and will help you stay on track.

Determine where you are

Lamentations 3:40 (NASB)

⁴⁰Let us examine and probe our ways, And let us return to the LORD.

1 Thessalonians 5:21 (NASB)

²¹But examine everything carefully; hold fast to that which is good;

Psalms 26:2 (NASB)

²Examine me, O LORD, and try me; Test my mind and my heart.

Identifying and assessing your financial situation

Before you can take action to improve your finances, you need to determine where you are financially. By recording the true numbers representing your financial situation, you will have a clear picture of where you need to start to improve your situation. Once you know exactly where you currently are, and as you will determine in later pages "where you want your finances to be," it will be easier to lay out a step by step-plan-to get you from point A (where you are) to point B (where you want to be). By filling in the following worksheets, you are on the road to improving your financial situation.

We all need guidance in evaluating our present financial situation. Our attitudes, and even our emotions, influence our spending patterns. It is for that reason that we must be *willing* to examine our motives and *pray* and *ask* God for guidance and direction. God has a plan for you!

It is *imperative* that husband and wife work together as a team on *their* financial plan—first examining your habits, and then assessing your financial position. The end result will be a plan both can live with. And the words you will use to describe this process are also important: It is not "my" plan or "your" plan, but "our" plan. Remember, a house divided against itself will not stand, but a house united cannot fail. Singles, don't feel left out—you need to go through the same process.

Personal property

A sample format for listing each item is as follows:

INVENTORY OF PERSONAL PROPERTY

Date Purchased	Item/Description	Original Cost	Current Value	Do Need	Don't Need
8/00	Sofa	$1,400	$600	X	
7/98	Rocking Chair	$350	$300		X
9/01	Table	$400	$200	X	
9/97	Camper	$9,000	$3,000		X
8/96	Fishing Boat	$5,000	$1,000	X	

Don't be concerned if you do not remember the original cost. List the item anyway with an approximate cost. This will help you see the relationship of cost to current value. In the future, list new items as you purchase them. A list such as this should be updated periodically, at least once each year, for insurance purposes if nothing else. Keep one copy of the list in a safe place. A safe deposit box at a bank, or a fire-proof box, would preserve the list and other important documents in case of fire. Sample forms for Inventory of Personal Property, Insurance Record, and Investments Record are included in the appendix. Transfer totals to the Asset Summary.

Sell those things you do not need

When you take an inventory of your personal property, you might ask yourself why you have each item and do you need it? For example, you might not go camping any longer since the children are grown, in which case you should ask yourself if it is wise to keep all of your camping equipment and gear. On the other hand, you may want to keep that fishing boat because you enjoy fishing with your spouse. Remember, it isn't enough to simply ask: "Do I need this?" Most people can justify to themselves a need when they consider a distant future. Instead, as you record each item on your list, honestly consider if you have used that item in the last six months or year. You should *sell those things that you do not need*, and use the funds to reduce your debts.

Inventory of Personal Property

Item Description	Original or Estimated Cost	Estimate of Current Value	Do Need	Don't Need
Total	$	$		

Insurance Record

Company Name	Type	Policy #	Amount of coverage	Annual Premium	Renewal Date
State Farm	Auto	12345	Liability	$1200	5/94

Investment Record

Name of Stock/ Bond Mutual Fund	Number of Shares	Date Purchased	Amount Paid	Current Value	Retirement Account

Asset Summary

Isaiah 44:24 (NLT)

24The LORD, your Redeemer and Creator, says: "I am the LORD, who made all things. I alone stretched out the heavens. By myself I made the earth and everything in it."

1 Timothy 6:17 (NASB)

17Instruct those who are rich in this present world not to be conceited or to fix their hope on the uncertainty of riches, but on God, who richly supplies us with all things to enjoy.

Step 1—Determine your assets

What are assets? Assets are all the things you own, including the money you have in the bank, your car, your home, your furniture, your investments, etc.

Liquid assets are items that can quickly be turned into cash.

Non-liquid assets are items that could take some time to liquidate or sell and turn into cash.

DATE PURCHASED	ITEM DESCRIPTION	ORIGINAL COST	CURRENT VALUE
1/xx		$23,400.00	$19,300.00
3/xx		$180,000.00	$230,000.00
6/xx		$598.00	$400.00

ASSESSMENT PHASE
DETERMINE WHAT YOU OWN
•ASSET ANALYSIS

ASSET ANALYSIS

•REVIEW EACH ITEM AND CONFIRM NEED

•IF NOT NEEDED, HOW COULD YOU SELL THE ITEM?

•IF NOT NEEDED, AND FINANCED, COULD THE ITEM
  BE SOLD FOR THE BALANCE OF THE DEBT OWED?

We recommend that you take a thorough inventory of every asset on an annual basis. Take out your latest bank statements, retirement account statements, etc. and fill out the asset summary in the following pages. Not all categories reflected will apply to you. Just fill in the ones which apply to your situation.

Asset summary

Liquid Assets

Cash on Hand & Checking Account(s)	$
Savings Account(s)	
Money Market Funds	
CDs	
Stocks	
Bonds	
Mutual Funds	
Savings Bonds	
Annuities (Cash Value)	
Life Insurance Cash Values	
Receivable From Others (Currently Due)	

Total Liquid Assets $ _____

Asset summary

Non-Liquid Assets

Home (Market Value)	$
Vacation Home (Market Value)	
Land (Market Value)	
Other Real Estate Investments (Value)	
Business (Value)	
Limited Partnerships (Value)	
Boat, Camper, etc. (Value)	
Automobile(s) (Market Value)	
Furniture & Personal Property (Estimated Market Value)	
Collectibles (Art, Coins, Stamps, etc.)	
Jewelry, Gold, Silver (Value)	
IRAs	
Other Retirement Funds	
Receivable From Others	

Total Non-Liquid Assets $ _____

Total Assets (Liquid+Non-liquid) $ _____

Step 2: Determine your liabilities

Proverbs 22:7 (NASB)

[7]The rich rules over the poor, And the borrower becomes the lender's slave.

Matthew 6:24 (NKJV)

[24]No one can serve two masters; for either he will hate the one and love the other, or else he will be loyal to the one and despise the other. You cannot serve God and mammon.

Romans 13:8 (NASB)

[8]Owe nothing to anyone except to love one another.

Your liabilities are all the debts you owe which, of course, include your unpaid bills and future payments that you do not owe on a monthly basis (i.e. car insurance policies can be paid every six months).

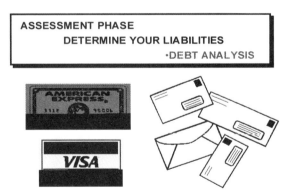

It should be your goal to reduce and eliminate your debt altogether as soon as possible. Your credit cards cost you more per month in interest than you can earn on most investments. Remember, *your best investment is your debt.* Don't consider implementing an investment program until all your credit card and installment debt is liquidated.

We recommend that you take a complete inventory of your debts or liabilities (what you owe). Use the last billing statement for each credit card and other loans to record the requested information on the Debt Analysis Schedule (next page). Include *all* liabilities: credit cards, car loans, debt for which you co-signed, etc.

Each billing statement should reflect the annual interest rate you are paying, the amount you still owe (your balance), and the amount and date of your next payment due. For each debt, list the name of the lender (creditor), the balance due, interest rate, payment per month and approximate date until the account is paid off. You can calculate the "approximate" date by taking the balance and dividing it by the monthly payment amount. The result will be the number of months it will take to pay off the balance (excluding the interest).

Your completed debt analysis schedule in many cases will be an eye-opener. Most people don't realize how much they owe and how long it can take to pay off all debts. Even if your debt falls within the "acceptable" range, from a worldly perspective, you may be making minimum payments until your 90th birthday.

LISTING YOUR LIABILITIES

A. INSTALLMENT LOANS

CREDIT CARDS

(a)
(b)
(c)

BANK LOANS

(a)
(b)
(c)

Your Debt Analysis Schedule

	Balance Due	Interest Rate	Monthly Amount	End Date
Installment debts and credit cards (creditors)				

Bank loans (creditor)

	Balance Due	Interest Rate	Monthly Amount	End Date

Total $ _____

Mortgages, loans and notes (creditor)

	Balance Due	Interest Rate	Monthly Amount	End Date

Unpaid bills (creditor)

	Balance Due	Interest Rate	Monthly Amount	End Date

Total $ _____

Total Liabilities $ _____

Step 3: Determine your net worth

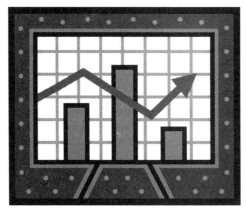

Matthew 6:33 (NASB)

[33]*But seek first His kingdom and His righteousness, and all these things will be added to you.*

Galatians 5:1 (NASB)

[1]*It was for freedom that Christ set us free; therefore keep standing firm and do not be subject again to a yoke of slavery.*

Your net worth is determined by subtracting your liabilities from your assets.

ASSESSMENT PHASE
DETERMINING WHERE YOU ARE?
•NET WORTH DETERMINATION

NET WORTH COMPUTATION

ASSETS MINUS LIABILITIES = NETWORTH

Your Net Worth

Total Assets (from Schedule - Page 22)	$

Less Liabilities:	
Liabilities (from Schedule - Page 25)	( )

Net Worth   ⊥_____

You can increase your net worth by increasing your assets and/or by decreasing your liabilities.

If your net worth increases at an average rate of 10% per year you are well on your way to financial success and prosperity.

Net Worth	Growth Rate	Time in Years	Accumulated Net Worth
$25,000	10%	25	$270,868
$25,000	15%	25	$822,974

$50,000	10%	25	$541,735
$50,000	15%	25	$1,645,948

Example:

Assuming you have total assets today (including your home) $220,000

Assuming you have liabilities as follows:

Mortgage	$150,000	
Auto loan	20,000	
Credit Cards	25,000	(195,000)
Net Worth		$ 25,000

Let's assume you eliminate your credit card debts within two years, and so increase your net worth by $25,000. Plus, during those two years you will have decreased your mortgage balance by, say $2,500 (principal reduction), your auto loan will have decreased by, say $10,000, and the value of your home increased by $12,500. Assuming these facts, your net worth will be $75,000. That is $50,000 higher than it was two years earlier—a 300% increase.

Apply a 10% increase to $75,000 for 25 years and your net worth will be $2,468,922.

Step 4: Determine your income

Ecclesiastes 5:19 (NASB)

¹⁹Furthermore, as for every man to whom God has given riches and wealth, He has also empowered him to eat from them and to receive his reward and rejoice in his labor; this is the gift of God.

Philippians 4:19 (NASB)

¹⁹And my God will supply all your needs according to His riches in glory in Christ Jesus.

Deuteronomy 8:18 (NASB)

¹⁸But you shall remember the LORD your God, for it is He who is giving you power to make wealth, that He may confirm His covenant which He swore to your fathers, as it is this day.

The next step in analyzing your current financial situation is to examine your monthly income.

Determine your average monthly income from all sources. For example, you might have wages and periodic income from a small business which you operate as a sideline. You may also have monthly income from a rental property. You may have some monthly interest or quarterly dividend income. The objective is to determine your total income from all sources on an average monthly basis.

On the Monthly Income from Wages/Salaries schedule, record your gross wages. Then record all payroll deductions to determine the net pay. It will help you account for your total income (before deductions), and analyze your deductions to understand where your earned wages are going.

ASSESSMENT PHASE
DETERMINING YOUR SOURCES OF INCOME
•INCOME SOURCES

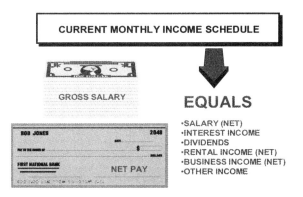

If your wages are not the same each month (like the income of a commissioned salesperson or seasonal employee), make some conservative estimate of your annual income and divide this sum by 12 to determine your average monthly income.

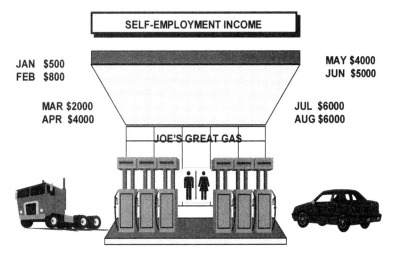

Please complete the following form: *Monthly Income from Wages/Salaries.*

Next, turn to the schedule *Current Monthly Income Schedule* to summarize your income from all sources.

Then proceed to the section *Current Income Evaluation.*

	Husband	Wife	Total
Gross Wages (Monthly)	$	$	$
Bonuses			
Total Gross Wages (Monthly)	T	T	T

Deductions From Pay (Monthly)

	Husband	Wife	Total
Federal Income Tax	( )	( )	( )
State Income Tax	( )	( )	( )
Social Security (FICA/Medicare)	( )	( )	( )
Pension Savings	( )	( )	( )
Medical/Dental Insurance	( )	( )	( )
Group Life Insurance	( )	( )	( )
Savings Bonds	(·)	( )	( )
Credit Union (Savings)	( )	( )	( )
Credit Union (Loans)	( )	( )	( )
Contributions	( )	( )	( )
	( )	( )	( )
	( )	( )	( )
	( )	( )	( )

Total Deductions From Pay	T( )	T( )	T( )

Net Wages (Monthly)	T	T	T

Current monthly income schedule

Periodic Income

	Amounts Received Periodically	Equivalent Amount Monthly	Regular Monthly Amounts	Total Monthly Amounts
Net Wages - Husband	$	$	$	$
Net Wages - Wife				
Dividends				
Dividends				
Dividends				
Interest				
Interest				
Interest				
Rents (Net)				
Business Income (Net)				
Pensions & Annuities				
Pensions & Annuities				
Social Security - Husband				
Social Security - Wife				

Total Monthly Income	T	T	T	T

Evaluating your income

Proverbs 20:5 (NLT)

5Though good advice lies deep within a person's heart, the wise will draw it out.

Proverbs 16:3 (NASB)

3Commit your works to the LORD And your plans will be established.

Ephesians 1:18 (NLT)

18I pray that your hearts will be flooded with light so that you can understand the wonderful future he has promised to those he called. I want you to realize what a rich and glorious inheritance he has given to his people.

Jeremiah 29:11 (NIV)

11 "For I know the plans I have for you," declares the LORD , "plans to prosper you and not to harm you, plans to give you hope and a future."

Did you know that approximately 80% of people are misemployed? Many people hate their job, and would tell you that they have never liked it much. Eventually, their dislike will show up in their attitude at work—the end result is that they either get fired or quit. Then, in total panic, they take the first job that comes along to save their "debt repayment plan." Needless to say, it won't be long before the cycle repeats itself.

If you are constantly changing jobs, are you ever really committed to your employer? Can you do your best at work when you are not committed to it?

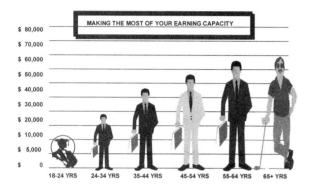

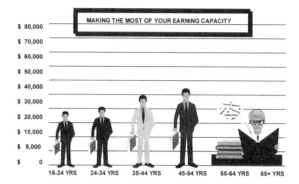

God has called you for His purpose. There is a calling on your life. God also provides you with talents to meet your calling. Do you know what your talents are? Do you know what your calling is? To find out, pray Ephesians 1:18 repeatedly and ask God for the answer. Paraphrased here, "I pray that the Lord may open the eyes of my heart that I may know the true purpose of His calling on my life." Once you know the purpose of His calling on your life, you can fine-tune your skills and move in the right direction. You will not only like your job, but God will bless everything you put your hands to. God wants you to work. Turn to Him for guidance in what He wants you to do. Then follow the path and you will be prosperous and have success.

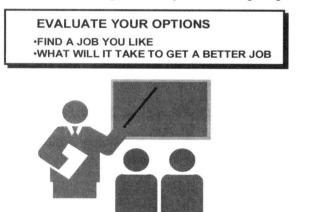

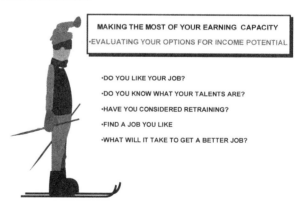

As you go through the worksheets on the following pages, prayerfully consider each question. Two copies have been provided so that each spouse can take the test separately.

Current Income Evaluation

Your Name_____

		YES	NO	NOT SURE
1.	Do I like the job I have?	____	___	_____
	Am I really doing the best I can?	____	___	_____
	Do I keep upgrading my skills?	____	___	_____
2.	Have I considered changing jobs?	____	___	_____
	Have I changed employment too often?	____	___	_____
	Have I tried everything to find a new job?	____	___	_____
3.	Do I know what my talents are?	____	___	_____
	Am I using my talents in my present job	____	___	_____
	Could I try to use my talents more effectively?	____	___	_____
4.	Am I willing to upgrade my education to get a better job?	____	___	_____
	Would I consider retraining?	____	___	_____
	Have I tried vocational counseling?	____	___	_____
5.	Have I tried to find a suitable job?	____	___	_____
	Have I been networking (asking, seeking, and knocking on doors)?	____	___	_____
6.	Do I believe it is important for me to work?	____	___	_____

Current Income Evaluation

Your Name_____

			YES	NO	NOT SURE
1.	Do I like the job I have?		____	___	_____
	Am I really doing the best I can?		____	___	_____
	Do I keep upgrading my skills?		____	___	_____
2.	Have I considered changing jobs?		____	___	_____
	Have I changed employment too often?		____	___	_____
	Have I tried everything to find a new job?		____	___	_____
3.	Do I know what my talents are?		____	___	_____
	Am I using my talents in my present job?		____	___	_____
	Could I try to use my talents more effectively?		____	___	_____
4.	Am I willing to upgrade my education to get a better job?		____	___	_____
	Would I consider retraining?		____	___	_____
	Have I tried vocational counseling?		____	___	_____
5.	Have I tried to find a suitable job?		____	___	_____
	Have I been networking (asking, seeking, and knocking on doors)?		____	___	_____
6.	Do I believe it is important for me to work?		____	___	_____

Step 5: Determine your expenditures

Galatians 5:16-17 (NIV)

[16]So I say, live by the Spirit, and you will not gratify the desires of the sinful nature. [17]For the sinful nature desires what is contrary to the Spirit, and the Spirit what is contrary to the sinful nature. They are in conflict with each other, so that you do not do what you want.

1 Corinthians 13:4-7 (NIV)

[4]Love is patient, love is kind. It does not envy, it does not boast, it is not proud. [5]It is not rude, it is not self-seeking, it is not easily angered, it keeps no record of wrongs. [6]Love does not delight in evil but rejoices with the truth. [7]It always protects, always trusts, always hopes, always perseveres.

Expenditures include all purchases, whether paid for with cash, by check, debit card, or credit card, and other amounts financed. In other words it is everything you have bought whether you've paid for it yet or not.

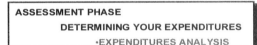

ASSESSMENT PHASE
DETERMINING YOUR EXPENDITURES
·EXPENDITURES ANALYSIS

Analyze and record your expenditures over the past three to six months. The purpose of this is to help you determine exactly how you spent your money. This exercise will provide you with much insight about your spending habits and priorities.

·PAYROLL DEDUCTIONS

·LIFESTYLE EXPENDITURES

·DISCRETIONARY EXPENDITURES

We recommend that you sort through the expenditures *one month at a time*. Be sure to use all credit card statements, bank statements, and your check books. Sort through the checks and group them by the expenditure categories provided in the "Expenditure Analysis Schedule" (additional sheets are available in the appendix). Indicate the month you are analyzing by entering it at the top of each of the four pages. For checks made out to "cash", do your best to remember or estimate how the cash was spent. If you have checks made out to cash, but don't remember how the cash was spent, enter a line "cash" under miscellaneous expenses. It *should* concern you that you do not know how you have spent your hard earned wages. Next, recap your credit card charges by expenditure categories and enter the results.

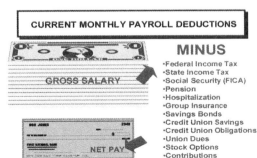

CURRENT MONTHLY PAYROLL DEDUCTIONS

GROSS SALARY

NET PAY

MINUS
·Federal Income Tax
·State Income Tax
·Social Security (FICA)
·Pension
·Hospitalization
·Group Insurance
·Savings Bonds
·Credit Union Savings
·Credit Union Obligations
·Union Dues
·Stock Options
·Contributions

It is important to *pray and ask God for guidance* throughout this analysis. Remember, it is necessary to review and understand your past spending habits, in order to later determine your future course of action.

Husband and wife need to do this exercise together! Remember, a house divided against itself will not stand, but a house united cannot fail. For singles, it is just as important for you to determine your expenditures and to know God's plan for your life. You might want to find a prayer partner to pray with you. There is power in prayer and He cares for you!

This process of sorting through your past expenditures together, husband and wife, can be very painful. Almost all couples experience difficulties when they go through this part of a financial plan. Here is what happens: the husband becomes defensive over the checks *he* wrote or the cash *he* spent, and the wife becomes just as defensive over the checks *she* wrote, or the cash *she* spent. It is a natural human response to become defensive about one's own actions. DO NOT GIVE UP!!

EXPENDITURES ANALYSIS SCHEDULE

The purpose of this analysis is not to point out actions of the past or to blame the other spouse for financial woes. It is important to remember we cannot change the past—it is history. But *together* we can learn from the past and forgive each other's mistakes. Pray together for God's guidance and help as you go through this exercise. *He has a plan for you.* He will help you come into agreement. Once you understand that the purpose of the exercise is not to pull you apart, but to bring you together into a common focus on your financial situation, then you will have weathered the storm.

It is important that you sort through as many months as it takes, one month at a time.

By the time you have sorted through six months, and have discussed and dealt with all the mistakes you discover, you should be able to discuss and deal with the future.

At this point, many couples experience for the first time a common purpose, a common financial perspective, and the basis to work together to reach their common financial goals —God's plan. He cares for you! ***As you go through this exercise, remember that the issue is not who spent the money, but rather how did we spend our money?***

We cannot undo a singe spending event of the past; we can only pay attention and change our future spending.

Expenditures Analysis Schedule

	(Month) Actual	(Month) Actual	(Month) Actual
HOUSING			
Housing (Rent/House Payment)	$	$	$
Insurance			
Property Taxes			
Water/Sewer			
Electricity			
Heating/Gas			
Telephone			
Sanitation			
Cleaning			
Repairs/Maintenance			
Supplies			
Improvements			
Furnishing			

Total Housing	$	$	$

	(Month) Actual	(Month) Actual	(Month) Actual
FOOD AND GENERAL SUPPLIES			
Food	$	$	$
General Household Supplies			
Entertaining			
School Lunches			
Lunches/Coffee Breaks			

Total Food & Gen. Supplies	$	$	$

	(Month) Actual	(Month) Actual	(Month) Actual
CLOTHING			
Husband	$	$	$
Wife			
Child			
Child			
Child			

Total Clothing	$	$	$

	(Month) Actual	(Month) Actual	(Month) Actual
TRANSPORTATION			
Auto Payments/Lease	$	$	$
Insurance			
Gas and Oil			
Repairs/Maintenance			
Licenses/Registration			
Parking			
Public Transportation			
Total Transportation	$	$	$

MEDICAL EXPENSES			
Health Insurance	$	$	$
Doctors			
Dentists			
Prescriptions/Drugs			
Total Health & Medical	$	$	$

INSURANCE			
Life	$	$	$
Disability			
Total Insurance	$	$	$

Entertainment and Recreation			
Eating Out	$	$	$
Baby-sitters			
Entertainment			
Vacations			
Travel/Short Trips			
Sports			
Hobbies			
Clubs/Dues/Activities			
Total Entertain/Recreation	$	$	$

	(Month) Actual	(Month) Actual	(Month) Actual
CONTRIBUTIONS & GIFTS			
Church	$	$	$
Missions			
Charities			
Total Contrib. and Gifts	$	$	$

	(Month) Actual	(Month) Actual	(Month) Actual
CHILDREN			
Allowances	$	$	$
Child Care			
Tuition			
School Activities			
School Supplies			
Total Children	$	$	$

	(Month) Actual	(Month) Actual	(Month) Actual
MISCELLANEOUS EXPENSES			
Gifts – Christmas	$	$	$
Gifts – Birthdays			
Gifts - Anniversaries			
Adult Education/Seminars			
Newspapers/Magazines			
Subscriptions/Books/Tapes			
Beauty & Barber			
Dry Cleaning/Laundry Service			
Stationery/Cards/Postage			
Total Misc. Expenses	$	$	$

	(Month) Actual	(Month) Actual	(Month) Actual
DEBT REPAYMENTS			
Credit Cards			
	$	$	$

Loans

Total Debt Repayments	$	$	$

SAVINGS & INVESTMENTS

Savings Account	$	$	$
Savings Bonds			
Mutual Funds			
Total Savings & Inv.	$	$	$

Total Expenditures	$	$	$

Evaluation

Proverbs 8:17-21 (NIV)

[17] I love those who love me, and those who seek me find me. [18] With me are riches and honor, enduring wealth and prosperity. [19] My fruit is better than fine gold; what I yield surpasses choice silver. [20] I walk in the way of righteousness, along the paths of justice, [21] bestowing wealth on those who love me and making their treasuries full.

1 Corinthians 4:2 (NIV)

[2]Now it is required that those who have been given a trust must prove faithful.

Current expenditures evaluation questions

	Yes	No	Not Sure
1. Do you know how much you can spend on housing?	___	___	_____
Do you know the advantages as well as the disadvantages of owning or renting a home?	___	___	_____

Advantages of owning a home

❋ Home ownership gives a sense of belonging and of security.

❋ Home ownership establishes a credit rating.

❋ Home ownership can generate a sense of enjoyment and satisfaction.

❋ Home ownership can create a valuable asset.

Financial Success Workbook

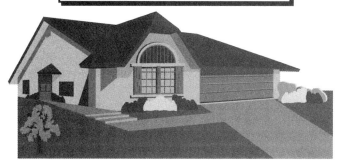

Disadvantages of owning a home

❊ The homeowner must assume responsibility for financing, maintenance, care and improvements; renters on the other hand leave those responsibilities to the owner or landlord.

❊ Home ownership may require larger monthly expenditures compared to renting when you consider upkeep, improvements, taxes and insurance.

❊ Real estate is subject to price fluctuations. The current cost may not be indicative of its future value

	Yes	No	Not Sure
1. Do you know which of your housing costs are fixed— meaning there is little opportunity for those costs changing?	—	—	———
Do you know which of your housing costs are controllable— meaning they can be changed more easily	—	—	———

An example of a *fixed and controllable* cost is your telephone bill. The basic charge for local service is fixed, while the long distance calls are controllable costs.

2. Are your food costs what you would like them to be?	—	—	———
Could you reduce your eating-out costs?	—	—	———
Should you eat out more often?	—	—	———
Are all lunches and coffee breaks important to you?	—	—	———
Does the school lunch program meet your needs?	—	—	———

	Yes	No	Not Sure

3. Do you have money to buy clothing when you need it?   ___ ___ _____
Could you save money monthly to meet seasonal
clothing needs?   ___ ___ _____
Could you cycle clothes from your older to
younger children?   ___ ___ _____
Are there other options, such as sewing skills?   ___ ___ _____

LEASING OR BUYING AN AUTOMOBILE

COST OF LEASING

COST OF BUYING

	Yes	No	Not Sure

4. Do you know what transportation options there
are in your community?   ___ ___ _____
Do you need a new car?   ___ ___ _____
Would a used car be sufficient?   ___ ___ _____
Do you know the true operating costs of your vehicles?   ___ ___ _____
Are you saving to buy or replace a car?   ___ ___ _____
Do you know what insurance coverage you have?   ___ ___ _____

LIFE INSURANCE
•TYPES OF PRODUCTS
•HOW MUCH IS ENOUGH

	Yes	No	Not Sure

5. Are you over-insured?   ___ ___ _____
Are you under-insured?   ___ ___ _____

MEDICAL INSURANCE

- •TYPES OF PRODUCTS
- •HOW MUCH IS ENOUGH

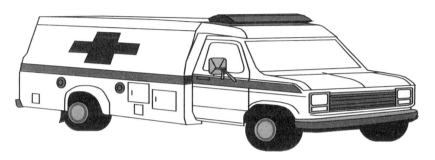

	Yes	No	Not Sure

6. Have you discussed your feelings about various insurance needs? ___ ___ _____
   Do you need to continue to spend money on "miscellaneous" items? ___ ___ _____
   Do you justify the present or future expenditures by the amount spent in the past? ___ ___ _____
   Do you know how to control these costs? ___ ___ _____
   Could you do more to control these costs? ___ ___ _____

7. Do you have a savings account? ___ ___ _____
   Do you save regularly for upcoming expenditures? ___ ___ _____
   Do you save regularly to buy replacements of appliances, car(s), or furniture? ___ ___ _____
   Could you save some if you tried? ___ ___ _____

8. Do you have investments? ___ ___ _____
   Do you need investments? ___ ___ _____
   Are your investments earning a good return? ___ ___ _____
   Do you know how much? ___ ___ _____
   Could you sell your investments to pay off debts? ___ ___ _____
   Could you sell them to set up savings accounts for upcoming expenditures and a reserve for replacements of large items, or an emergency fund? ___ ___ _____

Developing a household (or family) plan

Mark 3:25 (NASB)

²⁵ *If a house is divided against itself, that house will not be able to stand.*

Amos 3:3 (NIV)

³ Do two walk together unless they have agreed to do so?

Proverbs 6:6-8 (NIV)

⁶ *Go to the ant, you sluggard; consider its ways and be wise! It has no commander, no overseer or ruler, ⁸ yet it stores its provisions in summer and gathers its food at harvest.*

Why do we need a plan? We know that what we do today will have an effect on what we, or our family, will be like five years from now. Therefore, if we know what we, or our family, want to be like in five years, what can we do differently today? We can plan our course of action today to achieve our goals for the years ahead.

Without goals, people tend to be task-oriented rather than results-oriented. Goals are the end result toward which we intend to direct our efforts.

PLANNING PHASE

•RESOLVE TO LIVE WITHIN YOUR MEANS
•EVALUATE YOUR OPTIONS
•DEVELOP A LONG-TERM PLAN
•SET ATTAINABLE GOALS

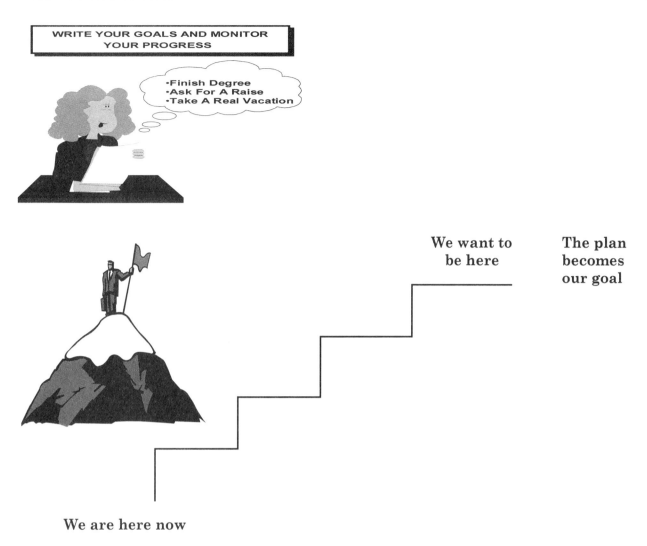

We get to where we want to be by taking steps and setting sub-goals. If we take our steps too fast, we run the risk of becoming discouraged. Often the desired long-range goals are not easy to achieve and require hard work and effort. Take one step at a time and allow yourself time to experience the joy of having reached each step. Remember, Rome was not built in a day! The sum of small efforts repeated day after day brings success. It is also important to write down your goals and sub-goals.

All of the knowledge in the world, without the determination to succeed, will be ineffective.

Setting financial goals

Luke 14:28-30 (NASB)

[28]For which one of you, when he wants to build a tower, does not first sit down and calculate the cost to see if he has enough to complete it? [29]Otherwise, when he has laid a foundation and is not able to finish, all who observe it begin to ridicule him, [30] saying, "This man began to build and was not able to finish."

Proverbs 4:26 (NIV)

[26] Make level paths for your feet and take only ways that are firm.

Proverbs 29:18 (NLT)

[18]When people do not accept divine guidance, they run wild. But whoever obeys the law is happy.

Habakkuk 2:2 (NLT)

[2]Then the LORD said to me, "Write my answer in large, clear letters on a tablet, so that a runner can read it and tell everyone else."

Financial goals are no different than any other goals. When we set them, we need to take action to start moving toward the desired result. If we set our goals too high at first, we set ourselves up to fail. For each goal, we should consider various sub-goals, or steps, which ultimately will add up to the achievement of each respective goal.

Suggested financial goals are

❋ Living within your means

❋ Planning to become debt-free

❋ Establishing a savings program

Spending habits are developed throughout your lifetime and are influenced by your family and societal patterns. It is important to remember that habits acquired over a lifetime are not changed overnight.

The following pages contain questions and guidelines to help you set financial goals, and to help you make some financial decisions. Remember to *pray* together for God's guidance. He has a *plan* for you. Most of all He *cares* for you!

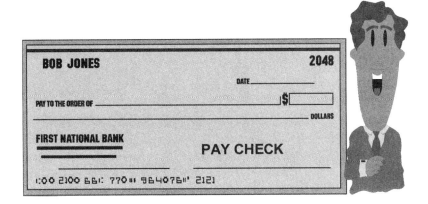

RESOLVE TO LIVE WITHIN YOUR MEANS
•MAKING THE MOST OF YOUR EARNING CAPACITY
•MAKING THE MOST OF WHAT YOU HAVE

Setting financial goals—evaluation questions

Living within your means

	Yes	No	Not Sure
1. Are you willing to live within your means?	—	—	———
2. Are you prepared to rearrange your spending priorities?	—	—	———
3. Have you sorted out and discussed the difference between?	—	—	———

Need—what you cannot do without or have to have
Want—what you should have, but could do without for a short time
Desire—what you would like to have but could do without

	Yes	No	Not Sure
4. Are you committed to do something about your financial problems no matter what?	—	—	———
5. Do you believe God can change this area of your life?	—	—	———
6. Could you increase your means (by looking for a better job, etc.)?	—	—	———

A plan to live within your means would necessitate the rearranging of spending priorities. You must be willing to change your spending habits and begin to live within your means today. If you wait until you get "caught up," you will not likely ever make it.

Two examples are given below of how rearranged priorities, given a chance, cannot fail and will succeed. The amount of income does not matter; the priorities must be the same.

	Example 1	Example 2
Salary per month	$ 3,000	$ 8,000
Taxes withheld	780	2,080
Net take-home pay	$ 2,220	$ 5,920
Tithing / Food / Shelter / Clothing / Other	1,800	4,700
Available for Debt Repayment and/or Savings	420	1,220

Planning to become debt-free

	Yes	No	Not Sure
1. Are you committed to getting out of debt?	___	___	_____
2. Do you agree to *pray*, and evaluate alternatives before borrowing again?	___	___	_____
3. Do you understand that co-signing is, in principle, the same as borrowing?	___	___	_____

A plan to become debt-free must include a plan to pay off all existing debt. When making extra payments on debt, it is wise to reduce the debt which bears the highest interest rate first. When one account is paid off, you shift that payment to another account until they are *all* paid off.

Example	Balance Owed	Payment	Interest
MasterCard	$700	$25	18%
Visa	850	40	16%
Loan Company	800	50	21%

Apply excess payments first to the "Loan Company" balance because they are charging 21%. When the loan is paid off, apply the $50 payment to MasterCard, paying them $75 per month. When MasterCard is paid off, make a payment of $115 to Visa until it is paid off.

Avoid overspending traps—overspending accumulates debt which has to be paid off sooner or later.

Behavior and attitudes—making adjustments in order to make lasting changes in your spending habits, you must become aware of the behaviors that trigger certain spending choices.

Changing spending-related behaviors is a continual process of recognizing problem situations and developing strategies to deal with them. It takes practice and positive reinforcement to develop new spending habits.

What situations trigger overspending for you?

_____

_____

_____

_____

_____

Establishing a Savings Program

	Yes	No	Not Sure
1. Do you have a savings account?	—	—	——
2. Do you save regularly?	—	—	——
3. Do you have a savings plan?	—	—	——
4. Do you know how much you could save per month?	—	—	——

A sound savings plan could consist of three types of savings. The first type is for known upcoming expenditures. An example would be the insurance on your home, assuming it is due annually. You could save 1/12 of that cost each month so that when the payment is due you have the money available in your savings account. A similar type of arrangement could be set up for your car insurance. Save 1/12 each month and when the payments come due you have the money available in your savings account. This type of saving can be referred to as "budgetary savings." You continually plan and save for the next 12 months. When one month is past you add another month to the plan.

The second type of saving is for replacements of large items such as car, appliances, home improvements, and for emergencies. It is suggested that you save each month a portion of the replacement cost of each item you expect to have to replace. Typically this involves small monthly amounts because the time to replace the next item may be several years off. Remember that the replacement cost will probably be greater than the cost of the original item. For emergencies, in case of a job loss or illness, it is suggested that you have a minimum of three to six months of household operating costs in reserve.

The third type of saving is for investment to meet college costs for the children and retirement needs. In today's financial system it is wise to plan for the future.

Saving on a regular basis takes discipline. It is a good habit which needs to be developed. Steady plodding brings success. Start with a little, be persistent, and you will succeed.

Your goals—write them down!

GOAL

_____

_____

COMMITMENT: I (we) make this commitment and will do the best I (we) can to reach this goal on or before _____, 20_____ .

OBSTACLES: These obstacles or roadblocks stand between us and our goal:

_____

_____

SOLUTION: We know that _nothing is impossible with God._ We will take the following action to overcome these roadblocks:

_____

_____

PROGRESS REPORT:

Date_____	Poor	Fair	Good	On target
Date_____	Poor	Fair	Good	On target
Date_____	Poor	Fair	Good	On target
Date_____	Poor	Fair	Good	On target
Date_____	Poor	Fair	Good	On target
Date_____	Poor	Fair	Good	On target

If at first you don't succeed, don't give up—try again!

Develop your spending plan

1 John 2:15-16 (NASB)

[15] Do not love the world nor the things in the world. If anyone loves the world, the love of the Father is not in him. [16]For all that is in the world, the lust of the flesh and the lust of the eyes and the boastful pride of life, is not from the Father, but is from the world.

Proverbs 3:5-6 (NASB)

[5]Trust in the LORD with all your heart And do not lean on your own understanding. [6]In all your ways acknowledge Him, And He will make your paths straight.

Psalms 32:8 (NIV)

[8] I will instruct you and teach you in the way you should go; I will counsel you and watch over you.

Your plan to live within your means requires that you budget your income and expenditures. The following pages are provided to help you establish a spending plan. If you have a family, discuss and consider each line item together. Remember, each family member (team member) should be able to provide input toward the spending plan.

When establishing a spending plan, you can approach the task by one of two basic methods.

A BUDGET AS YOUR GUIDELINE

•HISTORIC BUDGETING

•ZERO-BASE BUDGETING

Spending based on history

Review all past expenditures to determine the type of expenditure and current amount required. History serves as a guide for the future. For example, when budgeting for clothing, you can estimate how much you will need based on how much you have spent in the past, adjusted for cost increases. You justify future expenditures based on past costs incurred.

Zero-base spending plan

Without regard to past expenditures, determine what you are willing to spend in each category to operate your household. This may require you to change spending habits or alter your standard of living. For example, determine how much you want to spend in each category, within your spending limits; then make whatever changes that are necessary (even if it means moving to another home) to live within the spending plan. This approach does not justify the present or future by the past. Just because you have always done things a certain way does not mean that it is still in the best interest of your family plan and goals.

Another way of looking at zero-base spending plan is this: imagine you have just received a new job in a city 600 miles from where you lived. You know what your income will be, so you have to plan where you will live, what costs you can afford, and how much you will spend on each category at the new location in order to live within your means. You have a chance to start from scratch without regard to the current cost patterns.

The spending plan process

Have realistic expectations. Move along at a reasonable rate. Creating a spending plan is quite an accomplishment and it can be exciting to plan. However, speeding off in the wrong direction will get you nowhere fast—and can be dangerous. Remember that financial fitness is based on gradual, permanent changes in spending habits. Quick fixes bring quick results, but these results are usually short-lived as well.

This spending plan process is unique. It is important that you follow these instructions to get the maximum benefit from it.

First—Fill in the Budgeted Monthly Income from Wages/Salaries schedule. List your wages and payroll deductions. Make any adjustments to your payroll deductions you deem necessary. For example, if you usually receive a large tax refund, ask your accountant to calculate adjusted withholding taxes. This will result in higher net wages or net take-home pay.

Take the Net Wages and transfer them to the Budgeted Monthly Income Schedule.

If your income is from self employment and is not the same each month, make some conservative estimate of your net business income (total business income minus all business expenses). Divide the Business Income (Net) by 12 to determine your average monthly income.

For example:

January	$500
February	$800
March	$2,000
April	$4,000
May	$4,000
June	$5,000
July	$6,000
August	$6,000
September	$3,000
October	$1,000
November	$800
December	$500
Total	$33,600

Enter the total income in the Amounts Received Periodically column. Then divide the total annual income by 12, and enter in the Equivalent Amount Monthly column and in the Total Monthly Amounts column.

Budgeted monthly income schedule

Periodic Income

	Amounts Received Periodically	Equivalent Amount Monthly	Regular Monthly Amounts	Total Monthly Amounts
Net Wages - Husband	$	$	$	$
Net Wages - Wife				
Dividends				
Dividends				
Dividends				
Interest				
Interest				
Interest				
Rents (Net)				
Business Income (Net)				
Pensions & Annuities				
Pensions & Annuities				
Social Security - Husband				
Social Security - Wife				
Total Monthly Income	T	T	T	T

Second—Fill in the Schedule Of Amounts Paid Other Than Monthly. These are items which, if not planned for, are budget busters. For example, your car insurance may be due twice each year. If that is the case, unless you planned for this expense in advance, you might not have the money to pay for the premium.

This schedule reflects categories of expenditures which usually do not happen in equal monthly increments. For example, expenditures for clothing can be estimated by an annual amount, which is then divided by 12 to determine an equivalent monthly budget amount. Money is set aside each month so that when clothing purchases are needed, the money is there.

Vacation costs are often budget busters. Assume your vacation will cost you $3,000. If you set aside $250 per month, in twelve months you will have the amount you need. This concept is one most home owners are familiar with. They usually pay their property taxes and home owners insurance into an escrow account with the mortgage lender. When the taxes and insurance come due, the lender pays them from the escrow account.

On this schedule you determine the monthly amount that needs to be set aside on a regular basis. You transfer, or "spend" the amount each month to a savings account.

Enter the amounts so transferred to the Savings Account Summary.

For example, assuming your budget provides for you to save $100 per month toward your vacation and $20 for Christmas gifts, you would then write one check for $120 to transfer to your budgetary savings account.

The following is an excerpt on budgetary savings from the *Scriptural Principles: for Financial Success* in this series.

Budgetary Savings

Budgetary savings is an amount saved each month to cover planned and unplanned expenses that are not incurred equally each month. This type of saving is essential for an effective, functioning budget. For example, if car insurance premiums of $420 come due every six months, $70 per month needs to be saved. Failure to provide for budgetary savings is a budget buster and leads to borrowing. Saving for unexpected repairs fall into this category.

Budgetary savings also are used to even out seasonal expenditures, such as clothing. Annual clothing costs should be saved on a monthly basis until needed.

Budgetary savings also are used to even out large swings in income during the year. A school teacher may elect to be paid over nine months instead of having the salary paid out over twelve months. Each month a portion of the salary must be saved to carry the teacher through the three months when no salary is paid.

Construction workers and many self-employed individuals often find their income is uneven and/ or seasonal. They must utilize budgetary savings to even out the flow of money.

On the following schedule, enter the amounts transferred to your budgetary savings account, by category. Expenditures from the budgetary savings account are recorded in the same way. This schedule will show you the balance at the end of each month in your budgetary savings account and the individual amounts reserved for each category.

When you first start this process of saving for the amounts paid other than monthly, it may take you a few months to get this process up to speed. When you have the savings in place, it will make life a lot easier for you, as it eliminates budget busters.

Schedule of Amounts Paid Other Than Monthly

		Total Annual Amount	Average Monthly Amount
HOUSING	Insurance		
	Property Taxes		
	Repairs/Maintenance		
	Improvements		
	Furnishing		
CLOTHING	Husband		
	Wife		
	Child		
	Child		
	Child		
	Child		
TRANSPORTATION	Auto Replacement(s)		
	Insurance		
	Repairs/Maintenance		
	Licenses/Registration		
MEDICAL EXPENSES	Doctors		
	Dentists		
INSURANCE	Life		
RECREATION	Vacations		
	Travel/Short Trips		
	Sports		
	Hobbies		
	Clubs/Dues/Activities		
OTHER			
Total		$	$

Savings Account Summary
(for amounts paid other than monthly)

Month of _____, 20 ____

		Beginning Savings +	Current Savings −	Current Expenditure =	Ending Savings
HOUSING	Insurance				
	Property Taxes				
	Repairs/Maintenance				
	Improvements				
	Furnishing				
CLOTHING	Husband				
	Wife				
	Child				
	Child				
	Child				
	Child				
TRANS-PORTATION	Auto Replacement(s)				
	Insurance				
	Repairs/Maintenance				
	Licenses/Registration				
MEDICAL EXPENSES	Doctors				
	Dentists				
INSURANCE	Life				
RECREATION	Vacations				
	Travel/Short Trips				
	Sports				
	Hobbies				
	Clubs/Dues/Activities				
OTHER					
Total					

Third—the process of building your expenditures budget – PART I

The Expenditures Budget Worksheet shows four columns. Total, Need to Have, Should Have, and Would Like to Have. We will explain these columns later on. First, you should focus only on the Total column.

STEP 1—Transfer the monthly amount to be saved into your budgetary savings account from the Schedule Of Amounts Paid Other Than Monthly, by category, to the Expenditures Budget Worksheet (same categories) in the Total column.

STEP 2—Fill in all other amounts you want to budget for, also in the "Total" column of the Expenditures Budget Worksheet.

STEP 3—Add up the Total column in all four pages of the Expenditures Budget Worksheet to determine your TOTAL EXPENDITURES on a monthly basis.

Compare your Total Expenditures Budget to your income on the Budgeted Monthly Income Schedule. Usually, your budgeted expenditures will be much higher than your budgeted income.

Your objective is to live within your means! Now you need to do some soul searching. Why would you want to spend more than you have to spend and dig a hole for yourself?

Don't give up—there is hope!

In our book, *Scriptural Principles for Financial Success*, we discuss God's divine order for our financial priorities:

1. God

2. Taxes

3. Needs

The surplus above these three should first go to pay off our debt, before savings and investments.

In our personal finances Bible study guide, *Out of Debtor's Prison—A Roadmap For Debt-Free Living,* we discuss the problems of debt, steps to reduce and eliminate them, and how to get along without debt.

STEP 4 – Continue to go over the Total column of your budget and eliminate those items you cannot afford. Refer back to the discussion of Zero-base Budgeting above until your expenditures are equal to your budgeted income. Remember, overspending is not an option! You must choose to live within your means!

DO NOT PROCEED UNTIL YOUR BUDGETED EXPENDITURES EQUAL YOUR BUDGETED INCOME—THIS WILL MEAN THAT YOUR BUDGET IS IN BALANCE.

The following page is an adequate guideline for costs. *

Percentage for family income

Gross Income	$20,000	$30,000	$40,000	$50,000	$60,000
Tithe	10%	10%	10%	10%	10%
Taxes & Soc. Sec.	17%	18%	19%	22%	22%
Spendable Income	100%	100%	100%	100%	100%

	$20,000	$30,000	$40,000	$50,000	$60,000
Housing	35%	35%	30%	29%	26%
Food	20%	16%	13%	11%	10%
Clothing	5%	5%	5%	4%	4%
Transportation	13%	10%	9%	8%	7%
Enter./Rec.	6%	7%	7%	8%	8%
Medical Expenses	3%	3%	3%	3%	3%
Insurance	2%	3%	3%	3%	3%
Children	3%	2%	2%	2%	2%
Gifts	2%	2%	2%	2%	2%
Misc.	5%	5%	5%	5%	5%

	$20,000	$30,000	$40,000	$50,000	$60,000
Debt/Savings	5%	12%	21%	25%	30%

* Assumptions based on a family of four

The process of building your expenditures budget—part II

The four columns of the **Expenditures Budget Worksheets**—Total, Need to Have, Should Have, and Would Like to Have are defined below.

Total--*We assume that your budget is in balance, all items in the Total column in your Expenditure Budget Worksheets added up are your total expenditures and they equal your budgeted income.*

Need to Have—this represents an absolute need. It is what we cannot do without or what we must have.

Should Have—this represents amounts somewhat less important than an absolute need.

These are amounts we want or should have, but things we could do without in a pinch for a short period of time.

Would Like to Have—this represents amounts that are less important to you than an amount you absolutely need or want or should have. These amounts are based on choices or desires. They are what you would like to have, but could do without.

To help differentiate between the above levels of importance, focus for a moment on being unemployed. If you were suddenly unemployed, your income would be unemployment compensation. Most people would immediately switch to a "survival" mode and things that seemed impossible to live without yesterday have suddenly lost significance. It is with that flexibility you must approach your budget planning.

Negotiation process

Now all family members (team members) should be able to participate in the negotiation process for his/her needs. Remember, a united team cannot fail, but a divided team will not succeed. Determine for each amount in your budget whether it is an *absolute need* or an amount you *should have*, or whether it is an amount you *would like to have*.

Take each amount in the Total column and determine or negotiate how much of that total amount is an amount you *Need To Have*, how much of that amount is an amount you *Should Have* and last but not least, how much of that total amount is an amount you *Would Like To Have*. For example:

Budget category	Total	=	Need to have	+	Should have	+	Would like to have
Eating out	$200	=	$60	+	$90	+	$50
Telephone	$100	=	$35	+	$20	+	$45

Eating out—this may not be a *need* if you or your spouse enjoy cooking. However, knowing that there are times when your family schedule is overly demanding, eating out might be a necessity a few times each month in order to maintain sanity. So each category must be negotiated to blend individual needs into a realistic spending plan.

Telephone—perhaps the base amount is $35. Long distance calls which can be controlled are $65. Assuming a call to a sick parent from time to time is very important, but the total number of long distance charges may be as indicated after negotiation.

Initially you might think every item is an absolute need. Think again.

The more flexible you are in this process, the better your end result!

When all pages are filled in, add up each column. The total of the Total column must equal the totals of the three other columns. For example:

Total expenditures	=	Need to have	+	Should have	+	Would like to have
Total $4,000	=	$2,800	+	$800	+	$400

This exercise will build flexibility into your budget. Assuming you have an emergency where your car needs an unexpected repair, and you have not yet saved enough in your budgetary savings account to cover that repair. You are now able to look at your budget for this month and make a decision to take the amount you need first from the *Would Like To Have* categories and items, then from the *Should Have* categories and items.

You have already negotiated the importance of each item. It will be much easier to take from those categories and for the short-term redirect your money to cover the emergency without borrowing.

If these problems persist, it may be necessary to review how realistic you were when prioritizing your *Needs*, *Should Have* and *Would Like to Have* categories. You should also review your income budget and your options to increase your earnings. For some people, it may be necessary to reduce the *Needs* amounts. This may require moving to a smaller house or apartment. For others, less drastic steps will be sufficient.

Expenditures and budget worksheet

HOUSING	Total	Need To Have	Should Have	Would Like To Have
Housing (Rent/House Payment)	$	$	$	$
Insurance				
Property Taxes				
Water/Sewer				
Electricity				
Heating/Gas				
Telephone				
Sanitation				
Cleaning				
Repairs/Maintenance				
Supplies				
Improvements				
Furnishing				

Total Housing $ $ $ $

FOOD & GENERAL SUPPLIES

	Total	Need To Have	Should Have	Would Like To Have
Food	$	$	$	$
General Household Supplies				
Entertaining				
School Lunches				
Lunches/Coffee Breaks				

Total Food & Gen Supp $ $ $ $

CLOTHING

	Total	Need To Have	Should Have	Would Like To Have
Husband	$	$	$	$
Wife				
Child				
Child				
Child				
Child				

Total Clothing $ $ $ $

TRANSPORTATION	Total	Need To Have	Should Have	Would Like To Have
Auto Payments/Lease	$	$	$	$
Insurance				
Gas and Oil				
Repairs/Maintenance				
Licenses/Registration				
Parking				
Public Transportation				

Total Transportation $ $ $ $

MEDICAL EXPENSES

	Total	Need To Have	Should Have	Would Like To Have
Health Insurance	$	$	$	$
Doctors				
Dentists				
Prescriptions/Drugs				

Total Health & Medical $ $ $ $

INSURANCE

	Total	Need To Have	Should Have	Would Like To Have
Life	$	$	$	$
Disability				

Total Insurance $ $ $ $

RECREATION

	Total	Need To Have	Should Have	Would Like To Have
Eating Out	$	$	$	$
Baby-sitters				
Entertainment				
Vacations				
Travel/Short Trips				
Sports				
Hobbies				
Clubs/Dues/Activities				

Total Entert/Rec $ $ $ $

CONTRIBUTIONS & GIFTS	Total	Need To Have	Should Have	Would Like To Have
Church	$	$	$	$
Missions				
Charities				
Total Contrib. & Gifts	$	$	$	$

CHILDREN

	Total	Need To Have	Should Have	Would Like To Have
Allowances	$	$	$	$
Child Care				
Tuition				
School Activities				
School Supplies				
Total Children	$	$	$	$

MISCELLANEOUS EXPENSES

	Total	Need To Have	Should Have	Would Like To Have
Gifts - Christmas	$	$	$	$
Gifts - Birthdays				
Gifts - Anniversaries				
Adult Education/Seminars				
Newspapers/Magazines				
Subscriptions/Books/Tapes				
Beauty & Barber				
Dry Cleaning/Laundry Service				
Stationery/Cards/Postage				
Total Misc. Expenses	$	$	$	$

DEBT REPAYMENTS Credit Cards	Total	Need To Have	Should Have	Would Like To Have
	$	$	$	$

Loans

Total Debt Repayments $ ___ $ ___ $ ___ $ ___

SAVINGS & INVESTMENTS

	Total	Need To Have	Should Have	Would Like To Have
Savings Account	$	$	$	$
Savings Bonds				
Mutual Funds				

Total Savings & Investments $ ___ $ ___ $ ___ $ ___
Total Expenditures $ ___ $ ___ $ ___ $ ___

Monthly evaluations

A spending plan is only as good as the preparer's willingness to follow it.

Guidelines for follow-up

First—Complete the Monthly Summary and Evaluation Worksheet.

Any budget must be considered a guideline or plan for action. There always will be unexpected changes which have an impact on your plan. For example, car insurance rates may increase or decrease. So your plan must be flexible enough to accommodate the unforeseen. It is necessary to follow up to see how you are doing in comparison to the plan. Adjustments and compromises will have to be made from time to time.

To ensure the success of your budget, you need to examine and review each month—at the end—all of your actual expenditures and see how they compare to your budget. From your final spending plan, copy the Total column from pages 65-68 to the same items on pages 70-73. Then sort through your actual expenditures and repeat the process described on pages 36-37 for the Current Month. Then fill in the items on pages 70-73. There will be variances *over* and *under* the budget. Remember, no plan or budget is perfect— it is a guideline. Revise your budget as needed by repeating the process in the previous section of this workbook.

The amounts actually spent are entered in the Actual Amount column. The budgeted expenditures which are not presently due are "paid" into a savings account as if they were due. They also are entered in the Actual Amount column.

For example, assume your budget provides for you to save $100 per month toward your vacation. It also provides for saving $20 per month for homeowner's insurance. You would then write a check for $120 to your savings account. As your savings account accumulates funds, they are earmarked for predetermined purposes to the extent that this is the case.

Second—Complete the Savings Account Summary Worksheet.

Therefore, in addition to analyzing your actual expenditures as compared to your budgeted expenditures each month, you need to maintain an allocated breakdown of your savings account balance. A form is provided.

If at first you don't succeed, try, try again!

Refer to the Introduction describing your spending plan at the beginning of this book and re-read it periodically.

Monthly Summary and Evaluation
Month of_____, 20__

HOUSING

	Budgeted Amount	Actual Amount	Variance Over/(Under)
Housing (Rent/House Payment)	$	$	$
Insurance			
Property Taxes			
Water/Sewer			
Electricity			
Heating/Gas			
Telephone			
Sanitation			
Cleaning			
Repairs/Maintenance			
Supplies			
Improvements			
Furnishing			

Total Housing $ $ $

FOOD & GENERAL SUPPLIES

	Budgeted	Actual	Variance
Food	$	$	$
General Household Supplies			
Entertaining			
School Lunches			
Lunches/Coffee Breaks			

Total Food & Gen Supp $ $ $

CLOTHING

	Budgeted	Actual	Variance
Husband	$	$	$
Wife			
Child			
Child			
Child			
Child			

Total Clothing $ $ $

	Budgeted Amount	Actual Amount	Variance Over/(Under)
TRANSPORTATION			
Auto Payments/Lease	$	$	$
Insurance			
Gas and Oil			
Repairs/Maintenance			
Licenses/Registration			
Parking			
Public Transportation			

Total Transportation $ $ $

MEDICAL EXPENSES			
Health Insurance	$	$	$
Doctors			
Dentists			
Prescriptions/Drugs			

Total Health & Medical $ $ $

INSURANCE			
Life	$	$	$
Disability			

Total Insurance $ $ $

RECREATION			
Eating Out	$	$	$
Baby-sitters			
Entertainment			
Vacations			
Travel/Short Trips			
Sports			
Hobbies			
Clubs/Dues/Activities			

Total Entert/Rec $ $ $

	Budgeted Amount	Actual Amount	Variance Over/(Under)
CONTRIBUTIONS & GIFTS			
Church	$	$	$
Missions			
Charities			
Total Contrib. & Gifts	$	$	$
CHILDREN			
Allowances	$	$	$
Child Care			
Tuition			
School Activities			
School Supplies			
Total Children	$	$	$
MISCELLANEOUS EXPENSES			
Gifts - Christmas	$	$	$
Gifts - Birthdays			
Gifts - Anniversaries			
Adult Education/Seminars			
Newspapers/Magazines			
Subscriptions/Books/Tapes			
Beauty & Barber			
Dry Cleaning/Laundry Service			
Stationery/Cards/Postage			
Total Misc. Expenses	$	$	$

DEBT REPAYMENTS **Credit Cards**	Budgeted Amount	Actual Amount	Variance Over/(Under)
	$	$	$

Loans

Total Debt Repayments $ _____ $ _____ $ _____

SAVINGS & INVESTMENTS

	Budgeted	Actual	Variance
Savings Account	$	$	$
Savings Bonds			
Mutual Funds			

Total Savings & Investments $ _____ $ _____ $ _____

Total Expenditures   *$* _____   *$* _____   *$* _____

Savings Account Summary
(for amounts paid other than monthly)

Month of _____, 20 ____

		Beginning Savings +	Current Savings −	Current Expenditure =	Ending Savings
HOUSING	Insurance				
	Property Taxes				
	Repairs/Maintenance				
	Improvements				
	Furnishing				
CLOTHING	Husband				
	Wife				
	Child				
	Child				
	Child				
	Child				
TRANS-PORTATION	Auto Replacement(s)				
	Insurance				
	Repairs/Maintenance				
	Licenses/Registration				
MEDICAL EXPENSES	Doctors				
	Dentists				
INSURANCE	Life				
RECREATION	Vacations				
	Travel/Short Trips				
	Sports				
	Hobbies				
	Clubs/Dues/Activities				
OTHER					
Total					

Appendix

In This Appendix

* Expenditures analysis schedule

* Monthly summaries and evaluations

* Savings account summaries

Expenditures Analysis Schedule

	(Month) Actual	(Month) Actual	(Month) Actual
HOUSING			
Housing (Rent/House Payment)	$	$	$
Insurance			
Property Taxes			
Water/Sewer			
Electricity			
Heating/Gas			
Telephone			
Sanitation			
Cleaning			
Repairs/Maintenance			
Supplies			
Improvements			
Furnishing			

Total Housing $_____ $_____ $_____

FOOD AND GENERAL SUPPLIES			
Food	$	$	$
General Household Supplies			
Entertaining			
School Lunches			
Lunches/Coffee Breaks			

Total Food & Gen. Supplies $_____ $_____ $_____

CLOTHING			
Husband	$	$	$
Wife			
Child			
Child			
Child			
Child			

Total Clothing $_____ $_____ $_____

	(Month) Actual	(Month) Actual	(Month) Actual

TRANSPORTATION

Auto Payments/Lease	$	$	$
Insurance			
Gas and Oil			
Repairs/Maintenance			
Licenses/Registration			
Parking			
Public Transportation			

Total Transportation	$	$	$

MEDICAL EXPENSES

Health Insurance	$	$	$
Doctors			
Dentists			
Prescriptions/Drugs			
Total Health & Medical	$	$	$

INSURANCE

Life	$	$	$
Disability			
Total Insurance	$	$	$

Entertainment and Recreation

Eating Out	$	$	$
Baby-sitters			
Entertainment			
Vacations			
Travel/Short Trips			
Sports			
Hobbies			
Clubs/Dues/Activities			
Total Entertain/Recreation	$	$	$

	(Month) Actual	(Month) Actual	(Month) Actual
CONTRIBUTIONS & GIFTS			
Church	$	$	$
Missions			
Charities			

Total Contrib. and Gifts $ $ $

	(Month) Actual	(Month) Actual	(Month) Actual
CHILDREN			
Allowances	$	$	$
Child Care			
Tuition			
School Activities			
School Supplies			

Total Children $ $ $

MISCELLANEOUS EXPENSES

	(Month) Actual	(Month) Actual	(Month) Actual
Gifts – Christmas	$	$	$
Gifts – Birthdays			
Gifts - Anniversaries			
Adult Education/Seminars			
Newspapers/Magazines			
Subscriptions/Books/Tapes			
Beauty & Barber			
Dry Cleaning/Laundry Service			
Stationery/Cards/Postage			

Total Misc. Expenses $ $ $

	(Month) Actual	(Month) Actual	(Month) Actual

DEBT REPAYMENTS
Credit Cards

	$	$	$

Loans

Total Debt Repayments $ $ $

SAVINGS & INVESTMENTS

Savings Account	$	$	$
Savings Bonds			
Mutual Funds			

Total Savings & Inv. $ $ $

Total Expenditures $ $ $

Expenditures Analysis Schedule

HOUSING	(Month) Actual	(Month) Actual	(Month) Actual
Housing (Rent/House Payment)	$	$	$
Insurance			
Property Taxes			
Water/Sewer			
Electricity			
Heating/Gas			
Telephone			
Sanitation			
Cleaning			
Repairs/Maintenance			
Supplies			
Improvements			
Furnishing			

Total Housing $ $ $

FOOD AND GENERAL SUPPLIES

Food	$	$	$
General Household Supplies			
Entertaining			
School Lunches			
Lunches/Coffee Breaks			

Total Food & Gen. Supplies $ $ $

CLOTHING

Husband	$	$	$
Wife			
Child			
Child			
Child			

Total Clothing $ $ $

	(Month) Actual	(Month) Actual	(Month) Actual
TRANSPORTATION			
Auto Payments/Lease	$	$	$
Insurance			
Gas and Oil			
Repairs/Maintenance			
Licenses/Registration			
Parking			
Public Transportation			

Total Transportation	**$**	**$**	**$**

MEDICAL EXPENSES			
Health Insurance	$	$	$
Doctors			
Dentists			
Prescriptions/Drugs			
Total Health & Medical	**$**	**$**	**$**

INSURANCE			
Life	$	$	$
Disability			
Total Insurance	**$**	**$**	**$**

Entertainment and Recreation			
Eating Out	$	$	$
Baby-sitters			
Entertainment			
Vacations			
Travel/Short Trips			
Sports			
Hobbies			
Clubs/Dues/Activities			

Total Entertain/Recreation	**$**	**$**	**$**

	(Month) Actual	(Month) Actual	(Month) Actual
CONTRIBUTIONS & GIFTS			
Church	$	$	$
Missions			
Charities			
Total Contrib. and Gifts	$	$	$
CHILDREN			
Allowances			
Child Care			
Tuition			
School Activities			
School Supplies			
Total Children	$	$	$
MISCELLANEOUS EXPENSES			
Gifts – Christmas	$	$	$
Gifts – Birthdays			
Gifts - Anniversaries			
Adult Education/Seminars			
Newspapers/Magazines			
Subscriptions/Books/Tapes			
Beauty & Barber			
Dry Cleaning/Laundry Service			
Stationery/Cards/Postage			
Total Misc. Expenses	$	$	$

	(Month) Actual	(Month) Actual	(Month) Actual

DEBT REPAYMENTS
Credit Cards

	$	$	$

Loans

Total Debt Repayments | $ | $ | $

SAVINGS & INVESTMENTS

	(Month) Actual	(Month) Actual	(Month) Actual
Savings Account	$	$	$
Savings Bonds			
Mutual Funds			

Total Savings & Inv. | $ | $ | $

Total Expenditures | $ | $ | $

Monthly Summary and Evaluation

Month of_____, 20__

	Budgeted Amount	Actual Amount	Variance Over/(Under)
HOUSING			
Housing (Rent/House Payment)	$	$	$
Insurance			
Property Taxes			
Water/Sewer			
Electricity			
Heating/Gas			
Telephone			
Sanitation			
Cleaning			
Repairs/Maintenance			
Supplies			
Improvements			
Furnishing			

Total Housing $ $ $

	Budgeted Amount	Actual Amount	Variance Over/(Under)
FOOD & GENERAL SUPPLIES			
Food	$	$	$
General Household Supplies			
Entertaining			
School Lunches			
Lunches/Coffee Breaks			

Total Food & Gen Supp $ $ $

	Budgeted Amount	Actual Amount	Variance Over/(Under)
CLOTHING			
Husband	$	$	$
Wife			
Child			
Child			
Child			
Child			

Total Clothing $ $ $

	Budgeted Amount	Actual Amount	Variance Over/(Under)
TRANSPORTATION			
Auto Payments/Lease	$	$	$
Insurance			
Gas and Oil			
Repairs/Maintenance			
Licenses/Registration			
Parking			
Public Transportation			
Total Transportation	$	$	$
Medical Expenses			
Health Insurance	$	$	$
Doctors			
Dentists			
Prescriptions/Drugs			
Total Health & Medical	$	$	$
INSURANCE			
Life	$	$	$
Disability			
Total Insurance	$	$	$
RECREATION			
Eating Out	$	$	$
Baby-sitters			
Entertainment			
Vacations			
Travel/Short Trips			
Sports			
Hobbies			
Clubs/Dues/Activities			
Total Entert/Rec	$	$	$

	Budgeted Amount	Actual Amount	Variance Over/(Under)
CONTRIBUTIONS & GIFTS			
Church	$	$	$
Missions			
Charities			

Total Contrib. & Gifts	$	$	$

CHILDREN			
Allowances	$	$	$
Child Care			
Tuition			
School Activities			
School Supplies			

Total Children	$	$	$

MISCELLANEOUS EXPENSES			
Gifts - Christmas	$	$	$
Gifts - Birthdays			
Gifts - Anniversaries			
Adult Education/Seminars			
Newspapers/Magazines			
Subscriptions/Books/Tapes			
Beauty & Barber			
Dry Cleaning/Laundry Service			
Stationery/Cards/Postage			

Total Misc. Expenses	$	$	$

	Budgeted Amount	Actual Amount	Variance Over/(Under)
DEBT REPAYMENTS			
Credit Cards			
	$	$	$

Loans

Total Debt Repayments	$	$	$

SAVINGS & INVESTMENTS

	Budgeted	Actual	Variance
Savings Account	$	$	$
Savings Bonds			
Mutual Funds			
Total Savings & Investments	$	$	$
Total Expenditures	$	$	$

Monthly Summary and Evaluation

Month of_____, 20__

	Budgeted Amount	Actual Amount	Variance Over/(Under)
HOUSING			
Housing (Rent/House Payment)	$	$	$
Insurance			
Property Taxes			
Water/Sewer			
Electricity			
Heating/Gas			
Telephone			
Sanitation			
Cleaning			
Repairs/Maintenance			
Supplies			
Improvements			
Furnishing			

Total Housing $_____ $_____ $_____

FOOD &
GENERAL SUPPLIES

	Budgeted Amount	Actual Amount	Variance Over/(Under)
Food	$	$	$
General Household Supplies			
Entertaining			
School Lunches			
Lunches/Coffee Breaks			

Total Food & Gen Supp $_____ $_____ $_____

CLOTHING

	Budgeted Amount	Actual Amount	Variance Over/(Under)
Husband	$	$	$
Wife			
Child			
Child			
Child			
Child			

Total Clothing $_____ $_____ $_____

	Budgeted Amount	Actual Amount	Variance Over/(Under)
TRANSPORTATION			
Auto Payments/Lease	$	$	$
Insurance			
Gas and Oil			
Repairs/Maintenance			
Licenses/Registration			
Parking			
Public Transportation			

Total Transportation $_____ $_____ $_____

Medical Expenses			
Health Insurance	$	$	$
Doctors			
Dentists			
Prescriptions/Drugs			

Total Health & Medical $_____ $_____ $_____

INSURANCE			
Life	$	$	$
Disability			

Total Insurance $_____ $_____ $_____

RECREATION			
Eating Out	$	$	$
Baby-sitters			
Entertainment			
Vacations			
Travel/Short Trips			
Sports			
Hobbies			
Clubs/Dues/Activities			

Total Entert/Rec $_____ $_____ $_____

	Budgeted Amount	Actual Amount	Variance Over/(Under)
CONTRIBUTIONS & GIFTS			
Church	$	$	$
Missions			
Charities			
Total Contrib. & Gifts	$	$	$

	Budgeted Amount	Actual Amount	Variance Over/(Under)
CHILDREN			
Allowances	$	$	$
Child Care			
Tuition			
School Activities			
School Supplies			
Total Children	$	$	$

	Budgeted Amount	Actual Amount	Variance Over/(Under)
MISCELLANEOUS EXPENSES			
Gifts - Christmas	$	$	$
Gifts - Birthdays			
Gifts - Anniversaries			
Adult Education/Seminars			
Newspapers/Magazines			
Subscriptions/Books/Tapes			
Beauty & Barber			
Dry Cleaning/Laundry Service			
Stationery/Cards/Postage			
Total Misc. Expenses	$	$	$

	Budgeted Amount	Actual Amount	Variance Over/(Under)
DEBT REPAYMENTS			
Credit Cards			
	$	$	$

Loans

	Budgeted	Actual	Variance
Total Debt Repayments	$	$	$

SAVINGS & INVESTMENTS

	Budgeted	Actual	Variance
Savings Account	$	$	$
Savings Bonds			
Mutual Funds			
Total Savings & Investments	$	$	$
Total Expenditures	$	$	$

Monthly Summary and Evaluation

Month of_____, 20__

	Budgeted Amount	Actual Amount	Variance Over/(Under)
HOUSING			
Housing (Rent/House Payment)	$	$	$
Insurance			
Property Taxes			
Water/Sewer			
Electricity			
Heating/Gas			
Telephone			
Sanitation			
Cleaning			
Repairs/Maintenance			
Supplies			
Improvements			
Furnishing			
Total Housing	$	$	$

	Budgeted Amount	Actual Amount	Variance Over/(Under)
FOOD & GENERAL SUPPLIES			
Food	$	$	$
General Household Supplies			
Entertaining			
School Lunches			
Lunches/Coffee Breaks			
Total Food & Gen Supp	$	$	$

	Budgeted Amount	Actual Amount	Variance Over/(Under)
CLOTHING			
Husband	$	$	$
Wife			
Child			
Child			
Child			
Child			
Total Clothing	$	$	$

	Budgeted Amount	Actual Amount	Variance Over/(Under)
TRANSPORTATION			
Auto Payments/Lease	$	$	$
Insurance			
Gas and Oil			
Repairs/Maintenance			
Licenses/Registration			
Parking			
Public Transportation			

Total Transportation $ _____ $ _____ $ _____

Medical Expenses			
Health Insurance	$	$	$
Doctors			
Dentists			
Prescriptions/Drugs			

Total Health & Medical $ _____ $ _____ $ _____

INSURANCE			
Life	$	$	$
Disability			

Total Insurance $ _____ $ _____ $ _____

RECREATION			
Eating Out	$	$	$
Baby-sitters			
Entertainment			
Vacations			
Travel/Short Trips			
Sports			
Hobbies			
Clubs/Dues/Activities			

Total Entert/Rec $ _____ $ _____ $ _____

	Budgeted Amount	Actual Amount	Variance Over/(Under)
CONTRIBUTIONS & GIFTS			
Church	$	$	$
Missions			
Charities			
Total Contrib. & Gifts	$	$	$
CHILDREN			
Allowances	$	$	$
Child Care			
Tuition			
School Activities			
School Supplies			
Total Children	$	$	$
MISCELLANEOUS EXPENSES			
Gifts - Christmas	$	$	$
Gifts - Birthdays			
Gifts - Anniversaries			
Adult Education/Seminars			
Newspapers/Magazines			
Subscriptions/Books/Tapes			
Beauty & Barber			
Dry Cleaning/Laundry Service			
Stationery/Cards/Postage			
Total Misc. Expenses	$	$	$

	Budgeted Amount	Actual Amount	Variance Over/(Under)
DEBT REPAYMENTS			
Credit Cards			
	$	$	$

Loans

Total Debt Repayments	$	$	$

SAVINGS & INVESTMENTS

	Budgeted	Actual	Variance
Savings Account	$	$	$
Savings Bonds			
Mutual Funds			

Total Savings & Investments	$	$	$
Total Expenditures	$	$	$

Savings Account Summary
(for amounts paid other than monthly)

Month of _____, 20 ____

		Beginning Savings +	Current Savings −	Current Expenditure =	Ending Savings
HOUSING	Insurance				
	Property Taxes				
	Repairs/Maintenance				
	Improvements				
	Furnishing				
CLOTHING	Husband				
	Wife				
	Child				
	Child				
	Child				
	Child				
TRANS-PORTATION	Auto Replacement(s)				
	Insurance				
	Repairs/Maintenance				
	Licenses/Registration				
MEDICAL EXPENSES	Doctors				
	Dentists				
INSURANCE	Life				
RECREATION	Vacations				
	Travel/Short Trips				
	Sports				
	Hobbies				
	Clubs/Dues/Activities				
OTHER					
Total					

Savings Account Summary
(for amounts paid other than monthly)

Month of _____, 20 ____

		Beginning Savings +	Current Savings −	Current Expenditure =	Ending Savings
HOUSING	Insurance				
	Property Taxes				
	Repairs/Maintenance				
	Improvements				
	Furnishing				
CLOTHING	Husband				
	Wife				
	Child				
	Child				
	Child				
	Child				
TRANS-PORTATION	Auto Replacement(s)				
	Insurance				
	Repairs/Maintenance				
	Licenses/Registration				
MEDICAL EXPENSES	Doctors				
	Dentists				
INSURANCE	Life				
RECREATION	Vacations				
	Travel/Short Trips				
	Sports				
	Hobbies				
	Clubs/Dues/Activities				
OTHER					
Total					

Savings Account Summary
(for amounts paid other than monthly)

Month of _____, 20 ____

		Beginning Savings +	Current Savings −	Current Expenditure =	Ending Savings
HOUSING	Insurance				
	Property Taxes				
	Repairs/Maintenance				
	Improvements				
	Furnishing				
CLOTHING	Husband				
	Wife				
	Child				
	Child				
	Child				
	Child				
TRANS-PORTATION	Auto Replacement(s)				
	Insurance				
	Repairs/Maintenance				
	Licenses/Registration				
MEDICAL EXPENSES	Doctors				
	Dentists				
INSURANCE	Life				
RECREATION	Vacations				
	Travel/Short Trips				
	Sports				
	Hobbies				
	Clubs/Dues/Activities				
OTHER					
Total					

Other Books in the Abundant Freedom Series

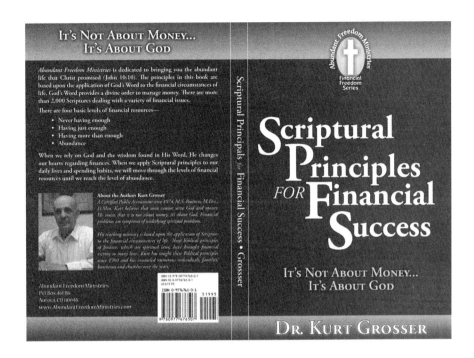

For further information about our Ministry and Publications visit our Web site,
www.AbundantFreedomMinistries.com
or write to Abundant Freedom Press,
P.O. Box 461316, Aurora, Colorado 80046